A Teddy Horsley Book

The Son

Teddy Horsley sings a song o

by Leslie J Francis and Nicola M S

Pictures by Laura Cooper

The Bear facts:
The Teddy Horsley Bible Series is designed to build bridges between the young child's day-to-day experiences of the world and major biblical themes and stories.

Both authors work in church-related institutions of education. Nicola Slee is Director of Studies at the Aston Training Scheme in Birmingham. Leslie Francis is Professor of Pastoral Theology at the University of Wales, Lampeter, and Trinity College, Carmarthen. The illustrator, Laura Cooper, is a teacher and artist.

The Teddy Horsley Series is a result of extensive research into the religious development of young children, and the authors' and illustrator's wide experience of educational work in schools and churches.

Published by:
National Christian Education Council
1020 Bristol Road
Selly Oak
Birmingham
B29 6LB

British Library Cataloguing in Publication Data:
A catalogue record for this book is available from the British Library.

First published 1984 Collins
Revised edition 1997

ISBN 0-7197-0901-6

Printed in England

Teddy Horsley pricks up his ears to hear the song of Creation.

He listens for the loud shout of the sun

and the soft whisper of the moon.

He hears the gentle patter of the rain

and the rough roar of the wind.

He hears the sharp crackle of the fire

and the crisp crunch of the snow.

He hears the patient purr of the cat

and the gruff growl of the dog.

He hears the bumbling buzz of the bees

and the colourful chorus of the birds.

Teddy Horsley hears the creatures of the Lord

sing God's praise and exalt God for ever.

He listens for the rich ring of the bell

and the mighty music of the organ.

He hears the clear words of the reader

and the peaceful prayer of the people.

He hears the cheerful choruses of the children

and the glad voices of the choir.

Teddy Horsley hears the creatures of the Lord

sing God's praises and exalt God for ever.

Teddy Horsley lifts up his voice to join in the song of Creation.

In *The Song,* Teddy Horsley listens to the many different sounds of creation praising God and the many different sounds of the Church praising God. Through this experience, he comes to share the sense of wonder and praise at the heart of Psalm 148.

Praise the Lord!

Praise the Lord from heaven,
    you that live in the heights above.
Praise him, all his angels,
    all his heavenly armies.

Praise him, sun and moon;
    praise him, shining stars.
Praise him, highest heavens,
    and the waters above the sky.

Let them all praise the name of the Lord!
He commanded, and they were created;
    by his command they were fixed in their places for ever,
and they cannot disobey.

Praise the Lord from the earth,
    sea-monsters and all ocean depths;
lightning and hail, snow and clouds,
    strong winds that obey his command.

Praise him, hills and mountains,
    fruit-trees and forests;
all animals, tame and wild,
    reptiles and birds.

Praise him, kings and all peoples,
    princes and all other rulers;
girls and young men,
    old people and children too.

Let them all praise the name of the Lord!

His name is greater than all others;
    his glory is above earth and heaven.

Psalm 148.1-13

The following questions suggest further ways of developing the links between the young child's experience, the story and the Bible passage.

Talk about the sounds of creation:

What sounds of creation can you hear if you go out into your garden or into a nearby park?

How many different kinds of weather can you think of that make different sounds?

How many different animals can you think of that make different sounds?

What different kinds of sounds do you like to make?

Talk about the story:

What different sounds of creation did Teddy Horsley hear in his garden?

What different sounds of creation did Teddy Horsley hear in his house?

What different sounds of creation did Teddy Horsley hear in the church?

Think some more about the story:

What other sounds of creation might Teddy Horsley hear in his garden?
What other sounds of creation might Teddy Horsley hear in his house?
What other sounds of creation might Teddy Horsley hear in the countryside?
What other sounds of creation might Teddy Horsley hear in the town?

Think about Psalm 148:

How many different kinds of sound can you find in Psalm 148?
How do you think the sun and moon praise God?
How do you think the lightning and hail praise God?
How do you think the winds praise God?
How many different ways can you think of praising God?

Titles in the series:

Autumn
Good Morning
Neighbours
The Picnic
The Walk
Do and Tell
Lights
Night Time
The Present
The Windy Day
Explorer
Music Makers
The Grumpy Day
The Sunny Morning
Water